AN ADOLESCENT'S GUIDE TO ME/CFS

VIDHIMA SHETTY

A Russian Hill Press Book
United States • United Kingdom • Australia

Russian Hill Press

ISBN: 9780999516232
Library of Congress Number: 2018948895

This book is dedicated to all the ME/CFS patients—rather, warriors—who deserve to have their voices heard. You have had to fight your own battles and on top of that, a society that is misunderstood or ignorant of the reality of this disease.

This book is especially for all the adolescents with ME/CFS. I hope this book finds you well, but please know that you are not alone in your struggle.

All profits from this book will be donated to the Open Medicine Foundation, an organization that focuses on advanced scientific research to find effective treatments and diagnostic markers for ME/CFS.

Contents

INTRODUCTION

Jane is a sixteen-year-old in high school. She's an organized girl who balances school with a social life, using the week to study for her classes and practice with her soccer team, and spending the weekend relaxing with her friends and pursuing some of her hobbies such as reading, writing, and biking. Whenever she can, Jane tries to volunteer at the animal shelter and the local food bank.

One day, Jane came down with the flu. She couldn't stop sneezing or sniffling her nose and often, she felt chills run through her body. At first, she ignored her symptoms and attempted to finish her math homework and study for the test she had in biology the following day. But as her symptoms worsened and she developed a fever, Jane found it too difficult to complete any of her school work. She was extremely weak, her muscles were sore, and her brain felt foggy. Because of her condition, she decided to stay home from school so she wouldn't spread the flu to any of her classmates and so she could recover as quickly as possible.

Four weeks passed since the day she got the flu, but Jane didn't feel like she had recovered from her illness. In fact, she felt worse than how she had initially felt when she had first gotten the flu: her body was constantly drained of energy and felt like a giant, limp noodle. Her head felt as if it was navigating through a dense fog, and she felt dizzy after taking a quick run around the park. Several hours after minimal physical activity or a brief period of studying, Jane would be unable to do any of her other work, feeling all her symptoms worsen even though she had barely done much. Her illness was unlike anything she previously had.

Despite these symptoms, Jane didn't visibly look like she was sick—not anymore, at least. So when she told her family about how she struggled to write a short story for her school's magazine, or complained about how her French class had felt like a blur, Jane's family found it difficult to believe.

The end of another week rolled around, and Jane forced herself to catch up on all the school work and volunteer activities she had missed. But now, she found that the tasks she had done daily—before she was sick—were harder for her to complete. She was out of breath after walking across the parking lot of the grocery store. She took ten minutes to finish one page of her favorite novel. She felt the immediate need to crash on the couch and sleep for the rest of the day after overworking herself at school. Even after sleeping, she didn't feel refreshed or resolved of her lack of energy.

Jane's health progressively worsened as time went on. Due to constant fatigue and her inability to keep up with school work, she dropped out of the school's soccer team and stopped volunteering at the animal shelter and food bank.

She consistently looked for excuses to avoid going to mall on the weekends with her friends or going roller skating with her little brother. Jane did not skip out because she didn't want to participate in those activities, but because she simply *couldn't*—she always felt mentally and physically drained. When her classes at school became too much of a burden to her health, Jane confided in her parents about her prolonged exhaustion.

In a haste, they took her to a doctor.

"She looks all right and doesn't appear to be in any pain," said the doctor. "What seems to be the trouble?"

"Jane always used to be full of energy and capable of participating in many activities, like sports, volunteering, and student council. But now, she finds it difficult to do even the simplest things," said her dad. "The other day, she was assigned to read a novel in her English class. Normally, Jane can finish a chapter or so in an hour. If she really likes the novel, she could probably read it in a single day. But now, it takes Jane an hour to read only two pages. She says she's too tired to keep reading and can't comprehend what's on the page. Some times, she'll continue to go through the book, but will forget what she read in the previous sentence or previous paragraph."

The doctor took a look at Jane and asked her how she was feeling.

"I'm just always exhausted and extremely weak," said Jane. "It's like my brain is foggy. It's hard for me to think or concentrate, and it's even harder for me to do the things that I used to do. I still feel like I haven't recovered from the flu that I came down with."

The doctor and Jane's family were left clueless.

"Take some ibuprofen and get some sleep," suggested the doctor. "Your body may just be overwhelmed by your schedule."

Even after she returned home and slept on and off for the next several days, Jane didn't feel any significant improvement in her health. In fact, over the course of the weeks that followed, her body only seemed to weaken. It was as if she were an electronic device with the battery consistently draining her. She was at the point where getting up to grab a snack left her feeling as tired as she would have felt if she had just run a mile. In addition, Jane developed more headaches and felt her brain become foggy at the slightest mental exertion. She became mildly sensitive to bright lights and couldn't tolerate loud noises.

So, what exactly was wrong with Jane?

WHAT IS ME/CFS?

What was happening to Jane? Why couldn't she shake off her exhaustion and recover from her sickness? Why was her brain constantly feeling foggy? Why did she feel so much worse after even small amounts of activity? Have other people gone through the same turn of events as she has?

After a year of visiting numerous doctors, Jane was finally able to meet one that was familiar with her condition. Once she had explained her core symptoms to this doctor, Jane was diagnosed as one of seventeen million people in the world that has myalgic encephalomyelitis (ME), which is also known as chronic fatigue syndrome (CFS), or in many cases, simply ME/CFS.

ME/CFS is a chronic, or long-term, complex, debilitating disease that causes those who suffer from it to miss out on normal lives.

But how does someone get ME/CFS? Is it contagious? How will having ME/CFS affect a person?

The answer to these questions, and many more, involves understanding what the disease entails.

A Note on Terminology

It is important to note that myalgic encephalomyelitis (ME) and chronic fatigue syndrome (CFS) were names developed to refer to separate outbreaks of the disease. The name "myalgic encephalomyelitis" was introduced after an outbreak of the disease in a London UK hospital in 1955.[1] The name "chronic fatigue syndrome" was coined following an outbreak in Nevada, USA, in 1984 to describe the number of individuals seen to be suffering from similar conditions.[2]

The label "chronic fatigue syndrome" was coined to avoid any assumptions about the etiology of the disease. This term, however, is considered by many to be a name that downplays the seriousness of the disease. For this reason, a 2015 report by the National Academy of Medicine (NAM) recommended that this term be retired.

"Myalgic encephalomyelitis," on the other hand, is a name that emphasizes an underlying physiological mechanism associated with the disease (it has been classified as a neurological disorder by the World Health Organization since 1969).[3] Breaking up the name gives one a better understanding of what ME refers to: myalgic (muscle pain), encephalo (brain), myel (spinal cord), and itis (inflammation). To clarify, the term indicates an inflammation of the brain and spinal cord, accompanied by muscle pain.[4] However, as of 2018, there has not yet been enough scientific evidence to prove that this neuroinflammation occurs within patients.[5]

Both "ME" and "CFS" have their own competing definitions and the different definitions encompass different patient populations. The definitions for CFS all require chronic fatigue and include mental illness but do not require hallmarks of the disease, such as the intolerance to exertion that Jane experienced. On the other hand, the definitions for ME all require the presence of the hallmark symptom of post-exertional malaise (discussed in the chapter What Are the Symptoms of ME/CFS?) but does not always require fatigue. Because of these differences in the definitions, the NAM stated that "a diagnosis of CFS is not equivalent to a diagnosis of ME." In other words, patients diagnosed with a CFS definition may not have the same disease as those diagnosed with an ME definition.

Ultimately, the issue of terminology leads to the lack of a conclusive definition of the disease. For the purposes of this book, the term "ME/CFS" will be used and refers to the disease described in the ME definitions and characterized by hallmark symptoms such as the intolerance to exertion.

ME/CFS in a Nutshell

ME/CFS is a complex and debilitating disease that profoundly affects and significantly limits the lives of patients. It is characterized by its core symptoms: overwhelming fatigue not relieved by rest, a substantial loss of physical and mental stamina, unrefreshing sleep, and post-exertional malaise (PEM), which is the worsening of symptoms after physical or mental exertion.[6] ME/CFS is also defined as a chronic, multi-system (affecting multiple body systems) disease that is associated with neurological, cognitive, autonomic, energy metabolism, and immunological dysfunction.[7]

Currently, ME/CFS does not have a pinpointed cause, a diagnostic test, a cure, or even an FDA-approved treatment specifically for ME/CFS. Though it is rare, recovery among patients is possible. However, recovery estimates in adult patients are as low as five to ten percent, and the majority of individuals suffering with ME/CFS will usually endure the disease for the extent of their lives.[8]

ME/CFS is a disease that is truly life-altering for all patients. The consequences of such an enfeebling disease have caused individuals with ME/CFS to collectively agree upon one statement: those who are afflicted with ME/CFS are robbed of their previous lives.

The Cold Facts

Worldwide, roughly seventeen to twenty-four million people have ME/CFS.[9] In the United States alone, there are about 1 to 2.5 million individuals that are said to have ME/CFS.[10] This number, however, cannot count as a precise value for how many people truly have the disease. In fact, studies estimate that about 84 to 91 percent of people with ME/CFS have not yet been diagnosed.[11] A UK study has also shown that 40 percent of patients with a diagnosis of CFS actually did not have the disease. Why is that?

There can be three reasons that account for these misdiagnosed or undiagnosed individuals:

1)   ME/CFS is a difficult disease to diagnose because it has no conclusive biomarker, or an indicator that is used to distinguish a certain disease or infection.

2)   Patients with the disease are often discounted of being sick because most of the time their symptoms are not visible to other people—physically, the patients that are able to visit healthcare professionals look like any average, healthy person would.

3)   Doctors themselves are unlikely to diagnose ME/CFS because they are unaware of the disease altogether or do not believe that it is real. Often times, cases that are brought to a physician's attention are dismissed as a psychiatric disorder or laziness.

The lack of knowledge about ME/CFS and the negative medical provider attitudes toward it prevent many patients from receiving the assistance they need to keep their health from worsening, or in some cases, from making gradual improvements and potential recoveries. In some instances, patients are harmed by doctors who prescribe inappropriate treatments that can make the patients worse.

To reduce the ignorance associated with ME/CFS, a select number of scientists are tirelessly researching the disease and are looking deeper into its biology, in hopes of understanding more about it.

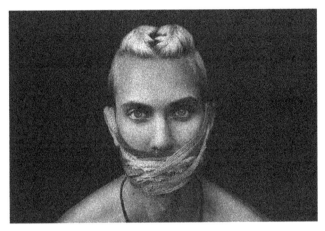

"Silenced"

An artistic visual of what it feels like to be an ME/CFS patient. Photo Courtesy of Sarah Allegra.

Photo courtesy of Ashanti Daniel

VOICES OF ME/CFS WARRIORS

Ashanti Daniel, 37, US

"This illness takes your life and flips it completely upside down."

Q: What was the progression of the illness like for you?

A: I got blindsided and was completely down by this illness from the very beginning. It started for me in August 2016, when I was working as a neonatal intensive care unit nurse. I suddenly became ill with respiratory symptoms. I do have a history of asthma, so everyone thought that this was a severe asthma exacerbation. Initially, I agreed that's what it probably was. However, when I was unresponsive to very aggressive treatment, I began to know that this was more than just asthma. I was very in touch with my body.

Prior to becoming ill, I was extremely healthy and extremely fit. I was working out four to five times a week, and did high-intensity interval training. I ate well, and I've always lived a healthy life. Everyone that knew me was dumbfounded that someone as healthy as I got so sick with this illness.

My last night shift was August 10, 2016. As the months have gone on, I've gotten progressively worse. And currently there are no FDA approved treatments, so everything is basically just trial and error. Unfortunately, my body has been resistant to everything that has been thrown at me.

I was officially diagnosed with having ME/CFS on ME international awareness day ironically—May 12, 2017. Currently I am housebound and I spend a lot of time bedbound. If I leave the house, I have to be in a wheelchair or motorized scooter. I am not even able to shower everyday—I'm lucky if I can shower twice a week. That's an accomplishment for me. I'm not even able to brush my teeth everyday. I stopped being able to drive eleven months ago. It's really a nightmare. I'm quite disabled with this illness.

Q: What are some of the hardships that you faced when you were struggling to understand that you had ME/CFS?

A: For me, I'd say I've been very blessed and am one of the fortunate ones (if there's such a thing with this illness). From the beginning, once I started sharing my story on social media about ME/CFS, and thankfully everyone has been supportive. The documentary, *Unrest*, has been a huge help with raising awareness and getting people to really see what this illness is about—what it's like to live with this illness.

There are times, though, when patients say to people that they're exhausted and usually they get a response with something like, "Oh yeah, me too." But the exhaustion that healthy people feel is nothing like what patients have felt. You're able to get up. You're able to get to your bathroom with no problem. You're able to shower, you're able to drive. You're able to do all these things that I cannot do because of my exhaustion. I've been sick for 20 months. During that time, there have been periods of various emotions—of course, loosing my career was like losing a part of my identity—it was very devastating. This illness takes your life and flips it completely upside down. I have a daughter in college and a son that is a teenager, so their lives have completely changed as well.

However, what I decided early on was that I may not have control over my body and the things that this illness was doing to it, but I have control over my mind. I've adopted an attitude of gratitude. I just try to focus on the blessings that I've had during this illness, instead of everything it has taken away from me.

Q: How would you describe having the disease to someone who doesn't know what ME/CFS is?
A: It's like having the worst flu you've ever had in your life multiplied by a million, plus being hungover

(or so I've heard people say) and running a marathon, all at once.

[This illness] does so many things to your body and it attacks so many systems that even the smallest or simplest things take so much effort. Your limbs feel like they weigh a thousand pounds each.

Q: What do you wish that people knew about ME/CFS patients?

A: I want people to understand that this illness is real and that it can impact everyone. It doesn't matter how old you are, what race you are, what your gender is, or what profession you have. Although I haven't personally experienced people disbelieving me, I know that the majority of the ME/CFS community has experienced this.

I also want people to know that [ME/CFS patients] still want to participate in life, but are often unable to. I tell people, (like Jen Brea had said in her film, *Unrest*) it's like you've died and you're forced to watch the world go on without you. You kind of exist and don't really live.

Q: What do you hope for the future of ME/CFS patients?

A: I hope that medical schools start educating more doctors (especially in the United States) about this disease. I think this will start shifting perspectives in the medical community about ME/CFS.

I hope more research for this disease will be

conducted. There needs to be more money allocated to researching this illness. And like any other patient, I hope for a cure.

A BRIEF HISTORY

Many people who hear about ME/CFS believe that it is the first time they have heard of the disease, raising the question: is it new? Is this some sort of disease that has appeared in the twenty-first century?

The answer is no. In fact, ME/CFS has been observed since at least the nineteenth century.

There is a chance that people haven't heard of it until recently, though, because over the past two centuries, outbreaks of the disease weren't identified under the term ME/CFS. In fact, the terms myalgic encephalomyelitis and chronic fatigue syndrome weren't coined until 1956 and 1988, respectively.

So then, what about all the years before that? How were cases of ME/CFS noted and recorded? It turns out that ME/CFS was identified in the past under multiple names—hence, it has also been called the "disease of a thousand names."[12] In 2015, for example, the NAM gave ME/CFS another name: systemic exertion intolerance disease.[13]

The earliest documentation of an "ME-like" condition in medical literature appeared in 1934 with the first reported outbreak in the United States occurring in Los Angeles, California, in the Los Angeles County General Hospital.[14] The disease that affected multiple patients (not known yet to be ME) did not spare the nurses and doctors of the hospital, who reported having muscle weakness, severe pain that was aggravated by exercise, and ataxia (the loss of control over bodily movements). Initially, it was thought that the disease was linked to poliomyelitis.[15] But this was later ruled out because unlike patients with poliomyelitis, the patients at the hospital who were affected by the disease did not have their muscles deteriorate, despite their weakness.

Following this incident, a number of other clusters of cases occurred that were similar to the Los Angeles outbreak. To mention a few, there were outbreaks in Akureyri, Iceland, where patients experienced fatigue and extreme muscle weakness, and in Fond-du-Lac, Wisconsin in the US, where a large group of people were diagnosed with encephalitis, or inflammation of the brain, although the cause of this outbreak still remains unknown.[16, 17]

One of the most widely-known outbreaks of the disease was in 1955, where a disorder that was present among many admitted patients of the Royal Free Hospital in Britain spread to the hospital's staff.[18] After an investigation of the obscure disease, health officials concluded that most patients had inflamed brains and spinal cords, although the cause of this inflammation was unknown. Following this, the term myalgic encephalomyelitis was adopted by the hospital's Infectious Diseases department, referring to the effect that the disease had on the body's muscles, brain, and nerves.

In 1959, Dr. Donald Henderson, a CDC epidemiologist, and Dr. Alexis Shelokov, an NIH epidemiologist, published a review summarizing 23 outbreaks of a similar disease in different parts of the world. These outbreaks had been given a variety of labels, such as "Iceland disease," and "atypical polio," among others. During the 1950s to the 1970s, these outbreaks, and others, were investigated in the US and given the name "epidemic neuromyaesthenia."[19]

By 1984, outbreaks of the illness had been seen in more worldwide locations such as Tapanui, New Zealand; Ottawa, Canada; Ayrshire, Scotland; and Durban, South Africa. An outbreak even made national headlines in the United States when it was discovered in Incline Village, Nevada, close to Lake Tahoe.[20] The disease, which was characterized by fatigue and neurologic disorders, initially affected only a small group of individuals within the town. Later, it spread to include more people within the community. Due to the fatigue and muscle weakness present in all patients, the disease was sometimes called the "Raggedy Ann Syndrome." Because of its impact, the Center for Disease Control & Prevention (CDC) was prompted to address the situation and to investigate the origins of the disease. Due to the CDC's dismissive view of the disease in Incline Village and lack of research, however, the scientific community was unable to determine what the disease's cause was.

Meanwhile, in 1978, a conference of international researchers had linked the disease myalgic encephalomyelitis, the term used in the UK, with epidemic neuromyasthenia, which, at the time was what the ME/CFS outbreaks were often referred to in the US, and had agreed to collectively adopt the term "ME." However, in 1988, the CDC decided to name the illness it had observed as "chronic fatigue syndrome" (CFS), overlooking the research by Dr. Henderson and the 1978 international conference.

Following the announcement of chronic fatigue syndrome, many individuals were opposed to this new terminology, because they felt that CFS disregarded the intensity of the disease and didn't include the effect that the disease had on the body's immune system. Therefore, the name "chronic fatigue immune dysfunction syndrome" was created. Today, however, "CFS" still remains considerably more popular than its counterpart.

Debates about the disease didn't stop there. A heated topic was whether CFS was simply a mental, rather than a physiological, condition. This debate started in the 1970s, when Dr. A.W. Beard and Dr. Colin McEvedy, psychologists at Middlesex Hospital in London, reviewed the notes from the outbreak of the disease at the Royal Free Hospital and decided that the observed epidemics were the result of "mass hysteria."[21] This reinterpretation of the outbreaks as not a physiological disease, but rather mass hysteria, was rejected by many physicians who had first-hand witnessed and treated the patients at the Royal Free Hospital.[22] Then in 1989, the idea that CFS was a psychological condition was further reinforced when Professor Simon Wessely promoted the disease as a mental illness. He believed that patients falsely thought they had a physical illness, and in turn, would become afraid of exercise and see themselves become deconditioned. To address this deconditioning, Wessely claimed that cognitive behavioral therapy (CBT), which is a type of psychological treatment, would be beneficial to patients by reversing their false beliefs of being sick. Although today it is known that the disease is not a mental illness, debates are still ongoing due to the ambiguous definitions of the disease and Wessely's disease theory, which has influenced both research and clinical care.

Throughout the history of ME/CFS, most observations of the disease have appeared in outbreaks. However, the last recorded outbreak of ME/CFS was in 1990s.

What happened? Why are there typically long

periods between outbreaks of the disease? Why do they occur in such randomized clusters?

The answer is unknown even to scientists. It is observed, though, that today the cases of ME/CFS are primarily seen as sporadic, individual cases and occasionally, in members of the same family.

Because of the debates about the disease and the cases in history that observed patients with a large range of symptoms, it took many years before a list of core symptoms for ME/CFS was finally developed and agreed upon.

Even though this list of core symptoms has been identified and maintained, there are many other aspects of the disease that are unknown or do not foster unanimous approval within the medical community.

One of these important aspects is the disease's cause.

Permission of anonymous owner

VOICES OF ME/CFS WARRIORS

Anonymous, 20, UK

"At this time, I was pushing myself through school and it nearly killed me. I kept ending up in the hospital, but I couldn't understand what was going on."

Q: What was the progression of the illness like for you?

A: I was living temporarily in Ethiopia, and I caught a variety of tropical diseases which I didn't recover from. This was the fall of 2014, part way between my seventeenth and eighteenth birthdays.

I haven't experienced the discrimination, prejudice, and the awful things that other patients have had to go through. I've had my fair of unpleasant doctors, but I count myself as lucky. I have an extremely caring doctor, but in the beginning it was a rocky start. I was totally confused and bewildered. I was very much in denial of having the disease—I just thought that it must have been stress of exams coming up, or anemia, or vitamin B deficiency.

At this time, I was pushing through at school, but it nearly killed me. I kept ending up in the hospital and I couldn't understand what was going on. So [my family and I] kept investigating with international doctors that were in Ethiopia, so that I could go back home.

At that point, I had done all the lab tests and heard many doctors say, "there's nothing wrong with you." I even had some doctors telling me that I might have an eating disorder, or that I was drinking too much alcohol—which I wasn't. There was this assumption that since I was a teenage girl, I must have been overdramatic or hysterical.

I was beginning to feel quite scared. But luckily my father, who's a policeman, had experience with people who had ME/CFS in the social care and mental health section, so he knew what it was. He suggested this to several doctors, but many of them immediately disagreed and said that it was impossible. There were other doctors who did believe in ME/CFS, but they had thought that I was too young to get the disease. I had even met with a rheumatologist, but when I told him I might have ME/CFS, he told me that for diseases like this, I would have to see a psychiatrist. I cried in the waiting room after that.

When I was back home in the UK, I met with my physician who went through as many blood tests as the national health system in the UK could provide. In this way, I had the possibility of other diseases excluded.

My deterioration from moderate to severe symptoms of the disease made me become bedbound. I can just about make it to the bathroom and back, if necessary. On good days, I can probably sit at the table for coffee. I'm up and active for about an hour each day, but I have to spend most of my time resting. I have to very carefully pace my activities and make careful choices asking myself: today can I dress myself? Can I have my hair washed? Unfortunately in my case, I can't do both of these things in the same day. If I try and push myself, I will relapse and the post-exertional malaise will be very intense and vicious.

Q: What are some of the hardships that you faced when you were struggling to understand that you had ME/CFS?

A: I would say that the time during my life [when I acquired the disease] was a very crucial point in my life, as it is for many people because between the ages of seventeen and eighteen. You're just about to go out into the world. I had all my universities lined up—I could've had the world at my feet, but it was all taken away from me. It was difficult to adjust to this massive life change and the process of acceptance.

As a young person, you're at that age where you're excited about going to university and moving out and living on your own. You have this newfound feeling of independence and freedom for the first time in your life. But these are things that you really lose with this disease. And if you're a severe patient, you certainly lose independence—you have to rely on your caregivers. In my case, my caregivers are my parents. I need them for just about everything—I can't go out on my own, I can't be left alone in the house for very long, and I can't even make it down and up the stairs. At points, it's very frustrating.

Another struggle I faced was when I was trying to get diagnosed. There was lots of hostile stigma associated with the disease and it was very unpleasant to experience. You're made to feel like you're a burden, or a liar. When people keep telling you, 'there's nothing wrong you,' you start to second-guess yourself and ask: Am I really ill? And this is the worst thing a patient can face. You're already so frightened and isolated.

Q: What do you wish people knew about ME/CFS patients?

A: I'd like people to know that [ME/CFS] is more than just tiredness. You can't take a nap and expect to feel better. It really has to be understood that this disease is complex and multi-systemic, affecting parts of the body that people don't even realize. This includes the autonomic function, cognitive function, heart rate, and blood pressure, among others.

A way that I would describe having ME/CFS to someone is comparing it to having the flu at all times. It feels like someone has filled all your bones with concrete, and you are being forced to run a marathon. It's soul-destroying. You can't lift your arms, your legs, or your head. Unfortunately, when you say you have chronic fatigue syndrome, people don't understand that you have to go through all of this. They don't understand that patients are confined to their beds or rooms for years.

Q: What do you hope for the future of ME/CFS patients?

A: I've talked to many other patients, and the sense that I get is that they're not even looking for a cure. They're looking for the medical community to believe them. We just want somebody to take notice and we would like adequate treatment. Of course, there are ongoing clinical trials, but we've got a long way to go.

I'm very hopeful that the "momentum" we've received from whatever publicity we've had so far will eventually help patients to be better treated.

WHAT CAUSES ME/CFS?

In the modern world, medical researchers have successfully traced the cause of many diseases to either bacteria, viruses, various organisms that invade the body, errors in genetic code, poor health habits, or assault on the body by environmental toxins. However, ME/CFS is one of the diseases whose cause scientists are still unclear about, because of the multiple ways that patients appear to have acquired it. Therefore, the topic of the disease's cause raises many questions: Is it inheritable? Is it contagious? Is it caused by bacteria or a virus? What causes it to start?

Possible Precursors

There are several factors that are believed to be possible triggers for the disease. Among ME/CFS patients, some of the observed preceding factors include viral or bacterial infections, exposure to a toxin, or an immunization (vaccine).[23] Some patients witness a sudden or acute onset (occurring within hours or days) while others have a gradual onset (occurring over months to years). Patients can also witness the onset of the disease following several of the possible precursors.

In many cases, it is common for patients with ME/CFS to feel as if they had caught the flu and never fully recovered from it. Remember Jane? She presented viral-like symptoms over the course of her illness and told her doctor that it felt like she still had the flu.

It is important to know, however, that not all ME/CFS patients observe the mentioned factors prior to the onset or development of the disease. Some patients, in fact, identify no precursor before the materialization of ME/CFS.[24]

Disease Theories

Today, there are multiple theories about the cause of ME/CFS. Some of these include immune abnormalities, neurological abnormalities, infectious agents, neuroendocrine disorders, metabolic disturbances, or genetic susceptibilities.[25] It may also be possible for a combination of these mechanisms to occur.[26] To simplify each of the theories' underlying mechanisms, it is easier to talk about them in regards to the symptoms they may contribute to.

Immune Abnormalities

One theory is that the symptoms of ME/CFS may be a result of immune system dysfunction. More specifically, symptoms may be an effect of a prolonged immune response, which is how the body recognizes and defends itself against bacteria, viruses, and substances that appear to be unfamiliar and harmful.[27] Normally, immune responses are temporarily activated, or self-limiting. After the body responds to an infectious agent, the immune response will turn itself off and return to its baseline state, or how it initially was before the appearance of harmful substances.

Studies in ME/CFS patients have shown that there are often changes within the immune system. Some of these changes include immune activation, deficient cell-mediated immunity (an immune response that does not involve antibodies), and decreased natural killer cell (NK) fuction.[28, 29, 30]

In ME/CFS patients, decreased NK activity has been an immunological finding. NK cells play an important part in the immune system because their function is to destroy cells that are infected with viruses. When the activity of these cells is reduced, the immune system is unable to eliminate new viruses. It is also unable to keep latent viruses, which are viruses that remain in a host organism without undergoing replication, under control. One study concluded that low NK cell activity was most likely consistent with flu-like symptoms and—possibly—the reactivation of latent viruses.[31]

Not all studies, however, have found a reduction of NK cell count in ME/CFS, and it can not yet be said that a decrease in NK cell count is a consistent finding among many patients. Researchers today are still looking further into this subject to find more conclusive results.

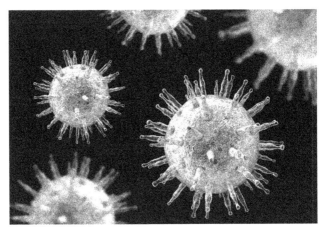

A computer illustration of Epstein-Barr virus.
Kateryna Kon/Shutterstock.com.

Infection

Today in most cases, ME/CFS commonly appears among individuals at random. But throughout the history of the disease (see more in the chapter A Brief History), many ME/CFS cases were seen to occur in cluster outbreaks. The hypothesis of microbial pathogens, which include viruses, bacterium, and parasites that can cause diseases, playing a role in ME/CFS is likely to support this observation.[32] Further belief for the assumption that infectious agents are involved in the disease is the flu-like symptoms that many ME/CFS patients have at disease onset.

The development of ME/CFS often follows an infection. A prominent example of this is seen with the Epstein-Barr Virus (EBV), which is a virus in the herpes family and is commonly known as the cause of infectious mononucleosis (glandular fever).[33] In addition, other infectious agents have also been found in patients and can play a role in influencing the severity of their symptoms.[34]

While infection is a common trigger of the disease, there continues to be a debate on the ongoing role of infectious agents over the course of the disease. This is due to the fact that no concrete evidence exists for whether there are active persistent infections within ME/CFS patients. Therefore, scientists are uncertain if there is a persistent replicating infection or if infectious agents have been eliminated, but gave rise to chronic symptoms as a consequence of a prolonged immune response.[35]

Neuroendocrine Disorders

The endocrine system is a collection of glands that secrete hormones directly into the circulatory system. Some of the major endocrine glands include the hypothalamus and pituitary glands (located in the brain) and the adrenal glands (located on top of the kidneys). When glands signal each other in a particular sequence, it is referred to as an "axis." A relevant example would be the hypothalamic-pituitary-adrenal (HPA) axis.

Similarities between the symptoms of ME/CFS and adrenal sufficiency (Addison's disease) such as excessive fatigue, was an area of interest for many scientists.[36] These similarities have prompted further research into abnormal HPA axis function within children and adult ME/CFS patients.

More thorough results are required (and are currently being looked at) if a connection between this hypothesis and ME/CFS can be made.

Metabolic Disturbances and Energy Metabolism Impairment

Some of the core symptoms of ME/CFS include overwhelming exhaustion and post-exertional malaise (PEM). Often times, patients (Jane, for example) experience an abnormal response to minimal physical and/or cognitive exertion that includes exacerbation of all symptoms and reduction in stamina and functioning.

In studies done of adult patients, observations were made that were relevant to the use of energy. One such observation was that the patients' bodies were not able to sufficiently consume oxygen.[37]

In the human body, mitochondria, which are the powerhouses for energy production, use oxygen to produce adenosine triphosphate (ATP). ATP is the molecule that generates cellular energy and is essential for bodily functions. When mitochondria are damaged, the levels of ATP significantly decline and the body runs out of energy.

The development of the theory that ME/CFS symptoms might be due to an issue in ATP production and mitochondrial transformation of energy stems from the findings of various studies.[38, 39]

Studies have also demonstrated that the symptom of PEM is associated with impairment in aerobic energy metabolism and a lowered anaerobic threshold. The exact role of energy metabolism impairment in the disease, however, is not yet clearly known.

Genetic Susceptibilities

Another theory is that the development, progression, or symptoms of ME/CFS may be related to genetic factors. It has been shown that in about 20 percent of patients, the disease affects more than one family member. In 90 percent of these specific cases where more than one family member is affected, the afflicted relatives were found to be more closely genetically related to one another than to other family members.[40, 41] Furthermore, a small study has shown that there may be a higher risk of acquiring ME/CFS among first-degree relatives.[42]

Gene studies in patients have also revealed interesting findings that may be correlated with symptoms of the disease. One study, for example, has shown changes in the expression of genes controlling apoptosis (programmed cell death), immune modulation, and oxidative stress.[43]

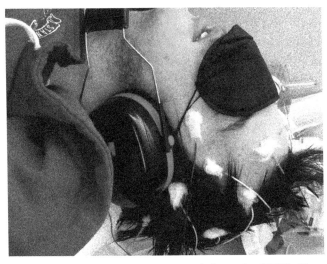

An ME/CFS patient has a electroencephalography (EEG). Photo courtesy of Dotty Camenzind.

Other Theories
Brain Dysfunction

Symptoms that are quite prominent among many ME/CFS patients is cognitive dysfunction (cognitive exertion is involved in reading, writing, or concentrating), neuroinflammation, lowered blood flow, and functional connectivity impairment. Neurological impairment includes reduction in blood flow to the brain, reduction in gray matter (a type of tissue in the brain) volume, and brain inflammation.[44] Therefore, many scientists have looked further into the hypothesis that abnormalities in the central nervous system (CNS) may be associated with ME/CFS.

Circulatory Abnormalities

It has been observed that in many ME/CFS patients, extended periods of upright posture can lead to lightheadedness and possibly other symptoms such as fatigue, cognitive dysfunction, and headaches. In a study that focused on possible circulatory abnormalities within ME/CFS patients, it was suggested that a link between the impairment of oxygen delivery to the brain and ME/CFS may exist.[45] In addition, low blood volumes have also been found among some adult patients with the disease.[46]

As the case is with almost all proposed theories, more research must be conducted in order to establish, if there are any, relationships between the hypothesis of circulatory abnormalities and ME/CFS.

ME/CFS: A Physical Disease

Despite all the theories and assumptions developed about ME/CFS, it has been collectively agreed upon—and proven[47]— that ME/CFS is not a mental or psychosomatic illness.

But even with plenty of demonstrable evidence, some people do not accept that ME/CFS is a physical illness. This disbelief undermines the disease and its severity, causing difficulty in the lives of many ME/CFS patients.

What Does This Mean?

The many theories that attempt to understand the

different ways of ME/CFS patients developing the disease may explain the variety of symptoms seen

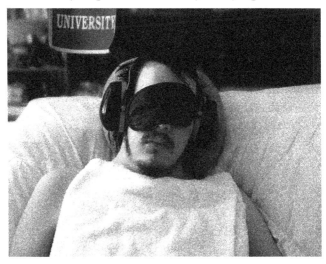

Photo courtesy of Dotty Camenzind

in patients. Unfortunately, it is these variations that make creating a universal prognosis, or a description of what changes and outcomes a disease will have over time, very difficult. As mentioned, onset of the illness in patients may be acute, or almost immediately happening, possibly following an infection, environmental toxin exposure, or another precursor. On the other hand, patients can endure a slow, gradual onset of the illness.

The course of ME/CFS is also unpredictable. Over time, the severity of symptoms may fluctuate for a patient and can be caused by over-exertion, additional illnesses, and additional factors.[48]

Because current theories are not able to account

for existing evidence, researchers and the ME/CFS community alike are coming up with more theories and more evidence as to why one possible hypothesis for the cause of the disease is more plausible over another hypothesis. Although, many of the mentioned theories have merit, there is the lack of one unifying theory that can tie them together.

However, there are cardinal symptoms of the disease that help identify who may have ME/CFS. Though many of these prominent symptoms have been

Is it Contagious?

In the cases where patients develop the disease sporadically, or without the influence of a group of afflicted individuals, ME/CFS is not thought to be passed on through casual contact.[49]

It is still not clear whether the disease is transmittable through any other forms. The CDC, however, recommends that ME/CFS patients refrain from donating blood.

mentioned through the discussion of what underlying mechanisms they may be associated with a more in-depth explanation of these symptoms are important to know.

WHAT ARE THE SYMPTOMS OF ME/CFS?

Remember Jane? She was constantly drained of energy, her brain felt as though it was foggy, she never felt refreshed even after sleeping for long periods, and she often felt dizzy and confused. She also lost significant functional capability after doing simple activities like cleaning her room and reading a book.

What about Jane led her to eventually being diagnosed with ME/CFS?

Since there is no biomarker or diagnostic test for ME/CFS, the only way Jane could be diagnosed was through her symptoms.

Usually, doctors are able to identify a disease through a characterizing set of symptoms that are common to all patients with that specific illness.

ME/CFS can be said to both follow and not follow this statement.

This is because although an ME/CFS diagnosis requires that patients experience certain core symptoms, each patient can have additional symptoms, which will vary from case to case. For example, Jane experienced fatigue, dizziness, abnormal responses to minimal physical and cognitive exertion, and unrefreshing sleep almost every day for many months. But another ME/CFS patient may report having all of the same symptoms as Jane *plus* abdominal pains and a swollen throat for a year. Regardless of this difference, both patients have been diagnosed with ME/CFS, not only because of their core symptoms, but also because of the frequency and severity of these symptoms.

But why exactly do ME/CFS patients have varying symptoms if they have the same disease?

The reason is likely to be found in human genetic susceptibility, differences in the micro-biome and metabolomics, and the varying triggers that lead to the disease to begin with.

In addition to having symptoms that can vary from one another, ME/CFS patients can also differ in the degree to which they show symptoms of the disease. For example, Jane was suffering from moderate symptoms of the disease where she had significantly reduced mobility and was unable to participate in daily activities. Another patient, however, could suffer from a more severe range of symptoms and become bedbound and sensitive to sound and light (more on this in the chapter Living with ME/CFS). It has also been observed that symptoms often fluctuate in intensity from day to day.[50]

Here are some of the core symptoms that appear in all ME/CFS patients.

Post-Exertional Malaise (PEM)

The core symptom of ME/CFS is "post-exertional malaise," (PEM) which is the body's abnormal response to minimal physical and/or cognitive activity. It is characterized by the worsening of some or all of a patient's symptoms and results in further loss of functional capacity for patients. (Patients often refer to their individual typical functional capacity as baseline and in PEM, a patient's level of function is markedly reduced beneath that baseline.) PEM is a hallmark of ME/CFS because this symptom is distinctive and relatively uncommon in other illnesses.[51]

To simplify the term, it can be broken down into two parts: post-exertional means occurring after exercise or any activity in which a person uses energy; malaise is a condition in which the body feels overall weakness and tiredness. The term malaise, however, falls short of the true meaning of PEM, because this symptom is not simply fatigue or tiredness. It is the reduction of a patient's level of function from both physical and cognitive effort. For some ME/CFS patients, walking across a parking lot is enough to cause PEM. For other patients, getting dressed in the morning or just brushing their teeth can cause the loss of typical functional capability and an exacerbation of symptoms seen in PEM.

PEM can begin immediately or more commonly is delayed several hours or days after a patient exerts himself or herself. This event, or trigger, need not be severe in order to cause severe PEM—in fact, there is no correlation between the severity of PEM and the intensity or duration of a trigger. The threshold for triggering ME/CFS, however, differs from patient to patient, and can even differ from one day to another in the same patient.

Recovery from these post-exertional symptoms also differ from patient to patient and is not relieved by rest. For some patients following some episodes, it may take about one to two days to recover. In other cases, it can take weeks, or even months to recover.

Cognitive Dysfunction and "Brain Fog"

Patients with ME/CFS usually have problems with short-term memory, which is the type of memory responsible for temporary storage of information, and working memory, which is the ability to process information and conduct tasks quickly. An example of short-term memory would be a person remembering what he or she had for breakfast in the morning. On the other hand, an example of long-term memory would be a person remembering the memory of their tenth birthday several years after it had happened. ME/CFS patients tend to have short-term memory loss more frequently than long-term memory loss.[52]

Patients also have problems with concentration and attention span. As a result, they may find simple tasks such as eating, walking, or speaking to be more stressful than they used to be. Additionally, patients have difficulty processing information. They may suffer from slowed thought, an inability to make decisions, disorientation, and confusion.

Cognitive dysfunction is often referred to as "brain fog."[53] The given term reflects the difficulty that patients have in thinking or remembering things. Sometimes patients mistake brain fog for headaches or exhaustion.

Sleep Disturbance

Non-refreshing patterns of sleep are primary symptoms of ME/CFS. Regardless of the duration of sleep, patients tend to awaken feeling exhausted or unrefreshed. In addition, patients can experience several types of sleep disorders including insomnia, and hypersomnia (excessive periods of sleep), among others.[54] The reversal of sleep rhythms is also common for ME/CFS patients. This reversal can result in patients sleeping throughout the day instead of during the night. Non-restorative sleep patterns are also usually frequent among patients.[55]

Orthostatic Intolerance

The simple meaning of this term is the difficulty or worsening of symptoms for a patient when he or she is standing or sitting upright. These symptoms are usually not apparent when lying down.[56] Orthostatic intolerance is often accompanied by lightheadedness, impaired concentration or focus, weakness, or fainting, among others.

Additional Symptoms

Pain: ME/CFS tends to cause muscle aches, joint pains that are without swelling or redness, headaches, or abdominal and chest pain.[57] This pain can be persistent and difficult to control but is not present in every case of the disease.

Other Possible Symptoms

- Muscle weakness
- Tender lymph nodes (small, bean-shaped groups of tissue located at the front and side of the neck, behind the ears, under the arms, and in the groin and abdomen)
- Sore throat
- Chills and night sweats
- Digestive issues (bloating, irritable bowel syndrome, etc.)
- Nausea
- Sensory sensitivity (sensitive to light, sound, touch, or smell)
- Double vision

For approximately 25 percent of people with ME/CFS, symptoms will be significantly more severe

and may include:
- Serious neurological symptoms (blackouts, loss of speech)
- Extreme sensory sensitivity, especially to noise, light, and touch
- Muscle wasting and weight loss
- Feeding via feeding tube

Patients with these severe conditions need the assistance of a caregiver and most often become bedbound due to the amplification of their symptoms.

How Do Physicians Today Diagnose Someone with ME/CFS?

Too often, ME/CFS has been mistaken to be a psychiatric illness. This is a misconception that has been promoted by a group of psychiatrists as discussed in the chapter A Brief History, and also stems from the fact that ME/CFS has no current conclusive biomarker, or indicator that is used to distinguish a certain disease or infection. Without the presence of a conclusive biomarker, diagnosing a disease becomes difficult to do.

Currently for ME/CFS, there is no valid, reliable laboratory test that can confirm a diagnosis of the disease.[58] Despite this, criteria for the disease has been developed for clinical diagnosis and for use in clinical practice.[59]

Although this book is by no means a substitute for a physician and will not go into depth as to how one can be diagnosed with ME/CFS, it will briefly look at some of the criteria that physicians can use to distinguish the disease.

Diagnosis for ME/CFS is a challenging process. In fact, it has often takes months or years for an individual to receive a definitive diagnosis.

In the past, to identify ME/CFS, physicians considered a diagnosis of exclusion.[60] As the name suggests, to diagnose patients, the process included identifying what diseases an individual didn't have. To rule out the possibility of a patient having a disease other than ME/CFS, physicians had to conduct numerous other tests.

Today, however, the National Academy of Medicine (NAM, previously called the Institute of Medicine) has created more specific clinical diagnostic criteria. According to the criteria, in order to make a diagnosis of ME/CFS, the presence of certain core symptoms are required[61]:

- A significant impairment in the ability to engage in activity that lasts six months or more, that is accompanied by fatigue, that is not lifelong, and that is not the result of ongoing exertion or significantly alleviated by rest
- Post-exertional malaise
- Non-refreshing sleep
- A manifestation of either or both cognitive dysfunction and orthostatic intolerance

In order to determine the presence of these

symptoms, the IOM suggested a set of targeted questions and recommendations for specific tests that physicians can use. Some of these tests can include.[62]

Tilt table tests (can help confirm if a patient has Postural Orthostatic Tachycardia Syndrome (POTS), which is a form of orthostatic intolerance)

- NK cell function test, an indicator of immune system impairment which studies have demonstrated are low in ME/CFS

- Two-day cardiopulmonary tests (CPET) (can be used to confirm the presence of PEM by assessing the performance of the heart and lungs at rest and during exercise)

- Neuropsychiatric testing (can be used to confirm the presence of cognitive dysfunction by showing impairment of the working memory and slowed information processing)

Now that some common symptoms in ME/CFS patients have been identified and the criteria for diagnosing these patients have been looked into, it's time to move on to some statistics.

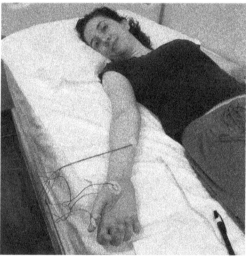

The amount of activity an ME/CFS patient can endure may vary from day to day. Brooke S. shows us that on some days a patient may be able to go out with family and friends (top photo). On other days, a patient may be confined to his or her bed (bottom photo). Photos courtesy of Brooke S.

VOICES OF ME/CFS WARRIORS

Brooke S., 29, US

"I wish people knew that nobody is helping us, that we are here, many of us living close to death and that we have to stay conscious for decades watching that."

Q: What was the progression of the illness like for you?

A: As a child I fairly was sick. I had constant ear infections requiring tubes in my ears and antibiotics. I had frequent high fevers. At twelve years old, I noticed I was increasingly tired and I struggled to stay awake in school. I started having problems with focus, concentration, and these symptoms gradually increased throughout high school. I did graduate and go to college fueled mainly by caffeine and energy drinks, although I still struggled a lot. I often did not know if I would make it. Looking back I can see that I was very sick, but at the time I thought that college was difficult and that I wasn't capable enough. It took all my energy to just sit up after I got home from classes and I started getting daily headaches. When I was young, at the doctor my labs didn't show anything. My family thought, maybe she is hypo-glycemic. They didn't know what to do since the doctors couldn't find anything.

In 2015, I went to graduate school at The London School of Economics. It would have been very difficult even for a healthy person. However, my fatigue started getting even worse. I had trouble processing lecture information or retaining it. I started forgetting commitments and details and times of things, missing meetings, assignments etc. I was very dependent on student-friends' help and became increasingly bedbound and isolated after classes.

Eventually, my symptoms became so severe that it was obvious that something was seriously wrong. In the second year of school, all symptoms were worse. I had problems understanding the lecture material, had increasing headaches and fatigue. I also developed new panic attacks with intense anxiety and felt faint and clammy. Towards the end of my first semester, I was completely bedbound for a week with heavy muscles and trouble moving around. I couldn't really leave my flat for two weeks. An MD noted iron deficiency and I was given iron supplements, but I was told nothing else was wrong. In 2017, I returned home to Arizona.

A physician suspected Epstein-Barr virus based on labs and symptoms but no treatment offered. She said all I could do was rest and try treating with vitamin IVs. I rested for two months but had no improvement and actually had worsening fatigue—I understand now that I had PEM. If I went out for a day, I was in bed for two to three days to recover. I had night sweats that were drenching, new dizziness and new orthostatic intolerance. I had difficulty eating and problems with motor control, was dropping things, breaking dishes, etc.

Q: How old were you when you initially got sick/how long has it been?

A: I was twelve. It has been seventeen years.

Q: What hardships did you face when you were struggling to understand what you had?

A: Doctors would say that they had patients who were really badly off and that I was wasting time. My family and friends tended to believe them. For the friends who did believe me, they didn't understand how serious it was and they struggled to communicate with me and to support me. When I would try and talk about what I was going through, but they would respond in a general way or change the subject which made me feel isolated and alone.

Q: What are some of the difficulties in everyday life that you face?

A: Getting to classes/food/meetings. In America, you can drive everywhere so I recovered a lot by just staying in my house and only walking to my car and driving to where I need to go. However, at university, the campus is big and there are not spaces to park a car. I got much worse when I started school because you have to walk everywhere, to class, to the dining hall, etc. Even taking my electric bike to class, the department building itself is huge and the elevator is always broken. I did speak with them about this but it took months to fix. As soon as it was fixed, it was broken again. They did offer to walk with me to the other elevator, but it would double the amount of walking I had to do. At school, I struggled to make friends because I could not leave my room. I also struggled to form study groups because I couldn't meet people which made the material harder to learn. I struggled to communicate with the school what I needed. There are risks to patients for pushing themselves too far. I was constantly weighing whether it was worth pushing myself to walk to class or to dinner, or if I would be doing permanent damage to my body by doing this. I thought, at some point having a life at all had to be more important than having the life I wanted and maybe it was better to come home.

Q: What do you wish people knew about ME/CFS patients in general?

A: I wish people knew that this disease is severe.

It has lower quality of life scores than MS/Cancer/etc. I also wish people knew that this disease is not rare, that it affects more people than AIDS, more people than MS.

I wish people knew that nobody is helping us, that we are here, many of us living close to death, and that we have to stay conscious for decades watching that. People have a tendency to think the system is genuinely good, that it works, and that it is fair. They think if there is a common disease that is very severe that it will get funding, but we have not had help for decades. I wish people knew that the system is not working.

WHO DOES ME/CFS AFFECT?

Who exactly gets ME/CFS? Is there a certain group of individuals that are likely to acquire the disease? Is it random?

Is there a chance that someone that you know might have the disease?

The answer to the last question, at least, is yes. There is a possibility that someone you know has ME/CFS.

The fact is ME/CFS does not predominantly strike a certain age, race, ethnicity, or socio-economic group—studies have reported that about 4 in every 1,000 adults have ME/CFS.[63]

In other words, anyone can get this disease. But there are certain observed trends among ME/CFS patients. For example, children, adolescents, and adults have been observed to be more likely to develop ME/CFS during certain age ranges.

#MeAction is an international network of ME/CFS patients, with the goal of bringing awareness to the disease. Photos courtesy of #MEAction.

Here are some statistics and trends among children, adolescents, and adults with ME/CFS.

Children and Adolescents

According to a 2006 study, the prevalence of ME/CFS among adolescents is about 0.18 percent.[64] ME/CFS in children younger than thirteen years old has not been a focus of many studies, but it is estimated that the prevalence rate of the disease in this age group is even lower than that of adolescents.

In children, cases of ME/CFS below the age of ten years old occur less frequently than adolescent cases, though the disease has been reported in those as young as five years old.[65, 66] It is true, however, that children on the younger side of the age range are rarely diagnosed with having ME/CFS. One reason among several can be because they have difficulty describing their symptoms or because some of their symptoms, such as cognitive dysfunction, could possibly be a result of other disorders, such as attention deficit disorder.[67] Though there is less data on the ratio of girls to boys that develop the disease, some studies have shown that ME/CFS in younger children is equally as likely to occur in either gender.[68]

On the other hand, a peak onset of symptoms occurs in adolescents during the ages of eleven to nineteen years old.[69] Unlike younger children (who have not gone through puberty), studies find that there is a greater prevalence of ME/CFS in adolescent girls, with approximately three to four times as many girls developing the disease than adolescent boys do.[70]

Since the peak onset of symptoms for adolescents are during the ages of when they attend higher educational institutes, many patients at this age may find themselves incapable of attending high school or college due to the severity of their symptoms. In fact, ME/CFS has been observed to be the most common reason for students to take a long-term sickness absence from school. [71, 72]

A deeper focus on ME/CFS among adolescents will be seen in *A Special Focus.*

Adults

ME/CFS has appeared more often in adults than any other age group. As previously mentioned, the prevalence rate of the disease in adults is close to four per every 1,000 individuals. In adults, the average age range for onset is between thirty to thirty-nine years of age.[73] The most common age for onset, though, is thirty-three years old. Although it is rare for older individuals to acquire ME/CFS, patients above the age of seventy have been diagnosed with the disease.[74]

Both males and females are affected by this condition, but research has shown that in ME/CFS adult women are three to four times as likely to get the disease than men.[75] Regardless of gender, however, the disease has been reported worldwide and across all ethnicities.

With the prevalence of this disease among the

The #BelieveMe project encourages patients to share photos of themselves in their daily lives. Photos courtesy of #MEAction.

the world's population, surely a cure must have been found, right?

Unfortunately, with ME/CFS, this doesn't happen to be the case.

Photo courtesy of Embla Lier

VOICES OF ME/CFS WARRIORS

Embla Lier, 21, Norway

"As a teenager, you're really trying to find yourself and your identity. Having ME/CFS makes that hard to do because the illness changes everything for you."

Q: What was the progression of the illness like for you?

A: In my case, I was fourteen when I had gotten pneumonia and mononucleosis. My health kept getting worse until I had to quit school. It really took me a year before I started looking very sick.

I had never heard about ME before I had gotten sick. My mother was the one who had mentioned it to me, and I had to search it up on Wikipedia to understand what it was. I took one look and saw the word "chronic" and I was shocked. I was basically denying the fact that I had this disease. But after seeing my doctor, it was clear that I had ME.

In the beginning I had thought that my condition would only last half a year and that I would be fine afterwards. But I didn't get better and I'm still sick. In retrospect, I didn't realize how sick I would be and how long it would last.

Q: What are some of the difficulties that you face with ME/CFS?

A: I'm kind of lucky, actually. I have the more moderate form of the disease, so I could do some things, but school was very hard for me. I could only attend part-time and I would have a lot of absences. I wouldn't do well on my tests because of this and my grades went down. My teachers also did not understand the disease and a lot of them thought I was faking my condition. I also couldn't go to social events—not hanging out with friends, not going to parties. I felt like a bit of an outsider.

I can almost compare having this disease to the grieving process. You have to give up many of your basic interests, ambitions, and dreams. Your entire life becomes very changed and it's like you are grieving for your life and the life that you could've had if you weren't sick.

Some days, I'm very accepting. I understand that this is my life. But other times, I think that this is not okay and that this isn't the way I want my life to be.

Q: What are some specific difficulties that you faced having the disease as a teenager?

A: When I got sick in the beginning, my parents didn't believe me. They thought that I had anxiety and that I didn't want to go to school or that I was being lazy because I was a teenager. So it took a long time before they started taking me seriously. Even at school, several teachers believed that I was just a bit stressed out and they didn't take me seriously at all.

As a teenager you're also really trying to find yourself and your identity. Being sick makes that hard to do because the illness changes everything for you. So I think that a lot of teenagers with ME/CFS feel very lost.

Q: How would you describe having the disease to someone who doesn't know what ME/CFS is?

A: One of the first things that I noticed when I got sick was that I thought I was getting sick over and over again, rather than having one big illness. This was primarily because there were so many symptoms and they would fluctuate a lot. So if I could describe it, I would say it is like being hungover while having the flu and not having slept in twenty-four hours all at once.

Q: What do you wish people knew about ME/CFS patients?

A: I wish people understood that we have both good and bad days and that the amount of things we do can each day will vary. Just because I did something last week doesn't mean that I can do that same thing today.

Q: What do you hope for the future of ME/CFS patients?

A: I hope people will know more about this disease—especially teachers and doctors. I would also hope that patients will have access to more medicines and that more research will be done in this area because there is not a lot right now to help patients.

THE SEARCH FOR A CURE

With many diseases, there is a standard set of recommendations that patients can follow to keep their health from deteriorating. Sometimes a doctor can prescribe medication or suggest therapies to attend.

For ME/CFS, unfortunately, there are currently no drugs or therapies approved by the U.S. Food and Drug Administration (FDA) for patient usage. In other words, there is no known cure for the disease yet. Worse, the most common therapies have been cognitive behavioral therapy (CBT) and graded exercise therapy (GET) based on the belief that patients have developed a fear of activity and have become deconditioned. The use of these therapies have recently been discredited and while some doctors may still recommend them, disease experts and the CDC do not.

Despite the lack of a universal cure, certain treatments and strategies can be used to help patients from seeing their symptoms worsen, and in other cases, to help relieve symptoms and improve their quality of life.

Current Treatments

Treatments today for ME/CFS are not substitutes for a cure, but they may help patients manage their illness, improve their quality of life, and avoid becoming worse. Current approaches to treating ME/CFS can be broken down into two main categories: disease modifying treatments and symptom alleviation and support.[76] Let's take a closer look at each category.

Disease Modifying Treatments

After some patients are accurately diagnosed by a clinician, they may decide (always, of course, by consulting with a clinician) to try treatments that address the mechanisms that may drive the illness. These mechanisms (as discussed in the chapter What Causes ME/CFS?) can include immune abnormalities, infections, and inflammation, among others.

Treatments that address these mechanisms can include anti-viral and anti-inflammatory medications or immunomodulators (which help to modify the activity in a patient's immune system).[77]

It is important to know that just as patients can show variations in the symptoms of ME/CFS they display, they can also respond to treatments differently.[78] While some patients may see an improvement of health, others may see no effect and some may feel their health worsen. To access these medications, patients must consult with a clinician. Unfortunately, because of the lack of ME/CFS specialists or knowledgeable clinicians and lack of research on these treatments, the consultations needed to identify the most appropriate treatment are difficult to secure.

Symptom Alleviation and Support

As a result, most patients are only able to use self-management to treat certain symptoms of the disease and sometimes are able to access doctors who prescribe medications that can alleviate their symptoms.[79] The variety of techniques—both learned and intuitive—that patients have used is described shortly in terms of what symptoms they usually help alleviate.

Relieving Lightheadedness

Some treatments that patients have used to treat the lightheadedness that accompanies orthostatic intolerance are increased electrolytes and salt and fluid intakes.[80] Both of these can help the body by increasing blood volume, thereby increasing blood flow to the heart and brain, and allowing a patient to avoid feeling lightheaded. However, this is not always enough and some patients may experience no lessening of lightheadedness even with treatment. In those cases, doctors can prescribe drugs that can help improve orthostatic intolerance.

Minimizing Post-Exertional Malaise

A key struggle that many patients experience is the "push and crash cycle."[81] This cycle is where patients who feel better on a given day, push themselves to do more than they would normally attempt, resulting in a "crash" and necessary rest. Remember Jane? After overworking herself at school, she came home and crashed on the couch. She rested herself for the next couple of days and once she started to feel a little bit better, she again began to overwork herself, eventually resulting in the same crash that she had felt before. Not only does this repeated exceeding of Jane's available energy cause her to relapse the next day, it can also cause a permanent worsening of her condition from which she may not get better.

All ME/CFS patients suffer from some form of PEM, whether it is mild (experiencing PEM after talking a walk around the neighborhood) or more severe (experiencing PEM after brushing teeth). PEM, in addition to causing loss of functionality, exacerbates a patient's other symptoms.

In order to avoid PEM, which is the resulting "crash" of the cycle, the "Energy Envelope Theory" was developed as a framework for self-pacing.[82] This method was founded on the idea that each ME/CFS patient is unique in the amount of energy that he or she can expend without crashing or pushing themselves beyond their physiological capabilities. By staying in their own physical safety zones and defining the amount of activity they can engage in, patients are able to minimize the frequency and severity of PEM. Staying within this zone can help to prevent further deterioration of health.

Ideally, doctors would be able to help patients learn how to pace and not push themselves beyond their safety zones, but because of the lack of ME/CFS specialists or doctors that are educated about the disease, patients may have to learn self-pacing methods on their own.

Relieving Depression and Anxiety

Patients with any chronic disease can suffer from depression or anxiety. People with ME/CFS who experience depression or anxiety may benefit from being referred to a mental health professional, who can accordingly prescribe medication like anti-depressants, if necessary. They may also benefit from deep breathing techniques or meditation, which they perform on their own and at their own pace.[83]

Improving Sleep

A key symptom that many people with ME/CFS observe is non-refreshing sleep. If possible, patients should visit their doctor and be tested for primary sleep disorder. If this disorder is present, it should be treated.

Patients may also improve their sleep through sleep hygiene, which is practices and habits that help people sleep well on a daily basis. However, generic sleep hygiene recommendations (no computers in bed, or bed only for sleep) may not be appropriate for patients who spend their days lying flat to avoid PEM. In some cases, patients can also be helped by sleep medications.

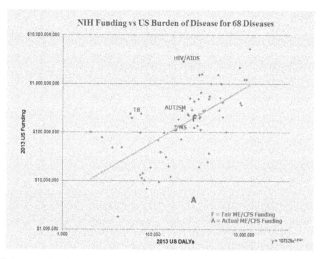

This graph depicts NIH funding for research dedicated to ME/CFS compared to the burden of the disease in the US (2013). Graph by ME Dimmock, AA Mirin, LA Jason from the Journal of Medicine and Therapeutics, 1 (2016)

The Reality of ME/CFS

The number of people that have been denied a

healthy, functioning life because of ME/CFS is startling. In fact, there are a number of reports that state that patients with ME/CFS have more functional impairment and lower quality of lives than patients with a number of other chronic diseases such as congestive heart failure, hyper-tension, and multiple sclerosis, among others.[84]

At first glance, the statistics may seem inaccurate because of the large number of people the disease affects. One might think, "If there's so many people with the disease, then why hasn't anything happened?"

To answer this question, there are several reasons that contribute to this problem: lack of awareness, widespread stigma and disbelief, an overemphasis on focus on psychiatric and psychological research to date, and a lack of funding for biomedical research.

Individuals with ME/CFS do not usually appear to be suffering from such a debilitating disease, unless, of course, they have a severe form the illness, in which most patients are bedbound and hence, out of the public eye. Even less severely ill patients typically do not leave their homes when their disease is at its worst. In adolescents who have ME/CFS and can attend school or a university, the disease is often overlooked due to age or the belief that the individual is exaggerating the reality of his or her symptoms.

Therefore, patients often receive a misdiagnosis or an underdiagnosis. Because these individuals don't appear sick when they leave home, doctors either do not recognize the disease or believe these patients have the disease. While there are currently diagnostic criteria to diagnose ME/CFS, the reality is that the medical community still doesn't actively use this criteria. Even if doctors say they adhere to the diagnostic criteria, they sometimes leave off critical details like PEM when diagnosing a patient, therefore conducting faulty diagnoses. Additionally, the general time allotted for doctors to spend with a patient is inadequate to cover the entire diagnosis process.

Prior to when the NAM created the current diagnostic criteria for ME/CFS, the medical community used loose diagnostic criteria that only required medically unexplained fatigue. This has also resulted in misdiagnoses where many patients have been sent to psychiatrists and are told that their disease is a result of a psychiatric illness. Doctors prescribe cognitive behavioral therapy (CBT), which has been studied and recommended in CFS to convince patients they are not sick, but instead are deconditioned. Doctors have also recommended graded exercise therapy (GET), which has been claimed to result in recovery. Often patients are told that exercise will alleviate their symptoms. In reality, this suggestion will only worsen an ME/CFS patient's conditions.

Because of historically poor disease criteria, the widespread acceptance of CBT and GET, and the lack of awareness for ME/CFS, many clinicians today are unable to properly diagnose and treat their patients. Imagine having to live with a disease that doctors don't believe is real!

In addition to a lack of awareness, biomedical research for ME/CFS is significantly underfunded. Institutions like the National Institutes of Health (NIH) and the Centers for Disease Control and Prevention (CDC) and governments are responsible for allocating funds for further research of diseases. According to a report by the National Academy of Medicine in 2015, ME/CFS is more common than multiple sclerosis (MS), lung cancer, or AIDS. During this same year, statistics showed that the amount of money spent for research per patient with MS ($255) or HIV/AIDS ($2,482) by the NIH, was far more than the amount spent for research per ME/CFS patient ($2). Although the current ME/CFS analysis shows that the total amount of money spent for research in 2017 was $14 million[85, 86]—certainly more than the $5 million that was spent in 2015—the estimated amount of funding that would be commensurate with disease burden (the amount of people that have the disease) is at $188 million.[87]

Because funding for ME/CFS hasn't improved enough within the past few years, many people are joining together to support the spread of awareness for the disease. Today, the community is demanding improved funding, a much more urgent response from the federal government, and a voice for ME/CFS patients. Campaigns and awareness days are held in recognition for the disease. People themselves are donating to foundations that support ME/CFS hoping

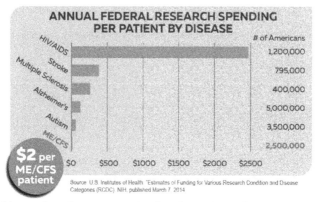

This graph estimates NIH funding for various diseases in 2014. U.S. Institutes of Health. Used with permission of Solve ME/CFS Initiative.

that researchers will be able to fulfill their tasks of finding conclusive biomarkers and a universal cure. By reading this book, even *you* are contributing to the promise of a better future for patients and their families.

LIVING WITH ME/CFS

After learning about the possible causes, symptoms, statistics, and many more relevant topics that discuss ME/CFS, one might wonder about the daily lives of patients. How do they cope with the disease? Are they ever able to do the activities they used to do before they acquired the disease? Is there a possibility for patients to recover?

Depending on how severe a patient's symptoms are, he or she will need to make changes accordingly. One patient may be able to carry on without as many changes to his or her lifestyle as another patient who can't tolerate the slightest sounds or lights and is bedbound.

So then, what can patients on both ends of the spectrum do to manage the disease, and what would their daily lifestyles look like?

The following sections allow people to see how

patients live with ME/CFS and what they can or already do to improve their health.

Mildly, Moderately, and Severely Ill Patients

All people with ME/CFS have had to make accommodations to their lifestyles. Patients that are considered mildly ill may still be able to work throughout the week. However, these individuals dedicate whatever spare time they can (the weekends, for example) to recovering. Because of this, they do not usually engage in an active social life and withdraw from many activities to spend time resting.[88] Just as any other ME/CFS patient, these individuals stay within their bodies' limits by pacing themselves so they don't end up crashing and can require less time to return to their pre-crash baseline health.

Patients that are moderately ill usually have significant reduced mobility and can be restricted from partaking in many daily activities. Most of these individuals are not able to work, but if they do, they are usually working part-time. Because of the increased need for sleep and rest, they will spend much more time in their houses. In fact, 25 percent of all patients are homebound or bedbound. The number of patients that are homebound or bedbound on their worst days of health are even higher. To account for their health, these individuals may only be able work for two hours per week or may have to switch to an online platform for education because of their inability to attend school.

Once in a while, moderately ill patients can have moments where their bodies feel less tired and the levels of their symptoms are minor, as compared to regular days with baseline symptoms. Unfortunately, some patients take their better days as opportunities to do more work or participate in more activities. This may lead patients to push their bodies beyond normal capacity and usually results in PEM.

On the other hand, these individuals can also have moments where they experience more severe symptoms. Like all patients, in order to maintain their health, they follow the Energy Envelope Theory (see the chapter The Search for a Cure) and do not push themselves beyond their physical threshold. Although the amount of activity (cognitive or physical) they can undertake without crashing (usually this is determined by trial-and-error) varies from day to day, they try to stay within their safety zones and do not overexert themselves. In addition, they take the same precautions that mildly ill patients do.

Severely ill patients are distinguished from mildly and moderately ill patients because these individuals usually require total care and are entirely dependent on a caregiver. They are either completely bedbound or are homebound, and can only carry out minimal tasks such as washing their hair or brushing their teeth.[89] Patients may suffer from severe symptoms such as extreme cognitive dysfunction and lack of mobility, which results in the need of a wheelchair. They may also be severely sensitive to sound and light (even more so than mildly or moderately ill patients), and in turn, wear eye masks and ear plugs to avoid exacerbating their conditions.

If they are able to secure the help of an ME/CFS specialist, those with severe ME/CFS are more careful with the drug treatments (if they choose to try them) their bodies undergo because they are usually more sensitive to medication. There have also been many reported cases where patients' symptoms have become more severe after treatments because of the drugs' side effects.

A Note About All ME/CFS Patients

Regardless of how ill a patient is, the chances of recovery from the disease are very slim with only a reported 5 to 10 percent of patients being able to regain the amount of function they could perform before they became ill. Instead, many patients have to manage ME/CFS throughout their lifetime, and as such, witness different levels of severity during the course of the disease.[90] It is additionally very difficult for patients to find clinicians that can diagnose ME/CFS. Therefore, even if it is ideal for patients to consult with specialists that can help them manage their illness, more often it is impossible for them to do so.

A Special Focus: Adolescents with ME/CFS

As a disease that critically affects millions of individuals around the world, ME/CFS has been observed to strike anyone, regardless of gender, ethnicity, socioeconomic status, or age.

Additionally, all patients have been seen to struggle with the illness in several ways, whether it means trying to maintain their health, receive an accurate diagnosis for the disease, adjust to such a debilitating disease, or convince others of the reality of ME/CFS.

There is, however, a group which the disease hits especially hard. These individuals have frequently been overlooked for having ME/CFS, are somewhat or entirely dependent on a caretaker (usually a parent or guardian), and frequently struggle to manage school with their illness.

When thinking about this group, you would be correct in remembering Jane.

Jane is one of the many adolescents that suffer from ME/CFS. Her circumstances are very similar to what many teenagers with the disease have encountered.

Before elaborating on the effects of the disease on adolescent patients, is it helpful to get a closer look into the statistics and prevalent observations about ME/CFS in these individuals.

Adolescent Patients and the Facts

After adults, adolescents are most likely to develop ME/CFS with the peak ages of onset appearing to be between eleven and nineteen years.[91] As previously mentioned, in this group, about three to four times as many girls have ME/CFS as boys do (covered in the chapter Who Does ME/CFS Affect?).

In these young patients, many recall the onset of ME/CFS after having an illness that resembles mononucleosis.[92] However, instead of recovering (mononucleosis usually lasts two to three weeks), patients usually see the development of the core symptoms of ME/CFS. Some of these include exhaustion, sore throat, lymph node pain, and abdominal pain, among other symptoms.

Unfortunately, many of these individuals are left in the dark about their disease. In a study done on ME/CFS patients between the ages of eleven and sixteen, it was observed that fewer than one in five adolescents who had the disease received a diagnosis or was offered treatment.[93]

A Note About Symptoms

Both adults and adolescent ME/CFS patients have a majority of the same symptoms mentioned in the chapter What Are the Symptoms of ME/CFS?, with the exception of a few differences. One is that in adolescents, abdominal pain and gastrointestinal impairments are more common.[94] Some adult patients never come across these symptoms throughout the course of the disease. Another difference is that in adolescents, facial flushing may be more common.[95]

As it has been observed in most ME/CFS patients, symptoms can significantly fluctuate on a day to day basis. One day, a patient may be able to go for a walk around the neighborhood. Another day, he or she may only be able to walk to the bathroom and back to bed.

Other Significant Effects of ME/CFS on Adolescent Patients

Being an adolescent with ME/CFS can often be very difficult. Many factors, such as age and body development, can impact the lives of these individuals. For example, puberty, a period of sexual growth and development, can affect an adolescent patient. If a patient acquires ME/CFS before puberty, it is possible that the disease can impact the physical and pubertal changes that an adolescent will undergo. In addition, it may affect his or her self-image.[96] On the other hand, if a patient acquires ME/CFS following puberty, it is possible that he or she may experience a delay in normal physiological development. More importantly, puberty can also exacerbate pre-existing symptoms of ME/CFS. In fact, adolescents (especially females) may be more prone to developing the disease after puberty.

Age is also a very relevant factor that usually impacts adolescents with ME/CFS. Often, a young patient can be overlooked for having a disease because others believe that he or she is faking or exaggerating his or her illness. Because many symptoms of ME/CFS do not visually translate on a patient, a medical practitioner may believe that an adolescent patient is faking his or her illness.[97] As a result, many young patients are left undiagnosed without any idea of what is happening to themselves.

A major aspect of an adolescent's life is their social life. Because of their condition, adolescent patients can have trouble attending social outings, family events, or gatherings.[98] Planning activities is also difficult for adolescents whose friends can't understand why they may be reluctant to commit to an activity or need to cancel plans at the last minute.

Another major aspect of an adolescent's life is an educational institution. ME/CFS, however, almost always affects the ability of a patient to regularly attend school.[99] Depending on the condition of the patient, he or she may be able to attend school daily, part-time, or unable to attend school altogether. Because of this, ME/CFS has been determined to be the most common reason for students to take a long-term sickness absence from school.

It is important to note that ME/CFS does not affect a patient's language ability or intellectual reasoning.[100] Instead, neurological impairments (most commonly brain fog) can impact a patient's ability to learn, often inducing forgetfulness or confusion. It can also cause a patient to have shorter attention spans and difficulty concentrating and processing information. As such, adolescents with ME/CFS often require a personalized learning schedule that allows them to manage schoolwork within the context of their illness. This may include allowing the patient to leave early or arrive late to school, have an independent study, or submit schoolwork online, among others.

Despite the conditions of these patients, unfortunately, many schools today are largely unaware of ME/CFS among students. Often, school nurses and educators do not understand the illness and are unable to provide necessary accommodations for a student suffering with ME/CFS. Although many individuals have taken efforts to acknowledge the disease among these institutions (such as creating fact sheets to inform nurses and educators[101]), the effect of ME/CFS on the lives of these young patients is yet to be fully recognized.

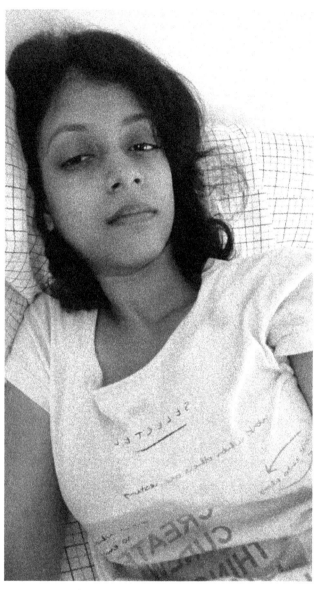

Photo courtesy of Michelle George

VOICES OF ME/CFS WARRIORS

Michelle George, 24, India

"I hope that people will understand that physical appearance is not a state of health."

Q: What was the progression of the illness like for you?

A: I fell ill when I was nineteen when I had first gotten chicken pox. Looking back, I realized that I had stayed in a room that was filled with mold. After this, I can say that I had begun to see several symptoms [that are familiar to ME/CFS], but it was really a year later that I had come down with a viral infection. This infection lasted for two months for me, and soon after I saw other symptoms. Specifically, I had sleep issues; I was sleeping for sixteen hours a day and I couldn't wake up to go to my classes. I also went through phases where I couldn't eat anything and would have symptoms similar to irritable bowel syndrome. The most prominent issue that I saw was fatigue. Back then, however, I didn't know what to call it; I just felt very sick.

I graduated college (with difficulty) a year later, still not knowing what it was that I had. The doctors had diagnosed me with depression and general anxiety. I didn't go to work, but instead I stayed at home. I spent most of my time researching what was wrong with me and initially thought I had celiac disease. I wasn't allowed to test if I had this disease, so I cut gluten from my diet instead. Because of this, the issues I had had with my stomach went away, but my fatigue and muscle weakness remained. I was really bummed at this point because after celiac disease, the only other disease I figured that I could have was ME/CFS.

Q: What are some hardships you faced?

A: Nobody around me understood that I was sick. On the outside, it looked like I was being lazy and many people thought that I was faking my illness. It also took a very long time for my parents to believe me—they thought that I had psychological problems so they took me to a psychiatrist. I was even put on medication, but obviously this didn't help.

Everyone also decided to take control of my life by looking for answers on the internet. People around me began to get mad, telling me that I should listen to a doctor and that I shouldn't be searching for answers online.

Now, however, more people are understanding because I have started to take control of my own narrative. I feel like I have a lot of knowledge about the subject and that I can speak up and say what is right for me.

Q: What are some difficulties of everyday life?

A: I want to do a PhD in neuroscience, but because of my illness, I feel that this is hard. Problems with cognition and memory affect me the most, so I can't quite recollect information. I get demotivated quickly because of this.

I have difficulty waking up everyday in the morning because I have sleeping problems. I generally cannot sleep during the night and I tend to sleep in the morning hours. I can be productive if I sleep in the morning but unfortunately, this isn't the way people work—life moves on in the daytime.

I can manage to do daily activities around the house. For example, I can cook for myself most of the time and probably do one or two more things before my energy levels are too low for me to do anything else. I spend a lot of time in my bed, on my laptop.

Q: What do you hope for the future of ME/CFS patients?

A: I hope that doctors begin to realize that this is a real disease. I feel like they should know more about

ME/CFS because the general public trusts doctors, and if doctors don't understand that this is a real disease, then neither will the general public.

I hope that people will understand that physical appearance is not a state of health. You may look sick or you may not look sick, but that doesn't show how you truly feel like on the inside.

WHAT SHOULD I DO IF I KNOW SOMEONE WITH ME/CFS?

By now, you've successfully educated yourself about a disease that affects millions of people around the world.

With the prevalence of ME/CFS, it may be possible that you have suspected someone around you or close to you has the disease. It also may be possible that this person does not know that he or she has ME/CFS.

So, the question is: what can *you* do about it?

The best answer is to educate these individuals and those around you. Only by knowing of this disease and what precautions must be taken in order to avoid the deterioration of health, will people with ME/CFS have any chance at recovering. Furthermore, if you believe that you know someone with ME/CFS that has not been diagnosed with the disease, urge him or her to visit a clinician.

Although there exists a lack of clinicians who can correctly diagnose people with ME/CFS, along with no known cause or cure for the disease, people with ME/CFS need not lose hope.

In the current day, there are educational efforts underway to teach doctors, an interest in starting clinical trials, and new advances in personalized medicine that may bring relief to those who must deal with ME/CFS symptoms on a daily basis.

#MillionsMissing is a global campaign that spreads awareness about the reality of ME/CFS and the affect that it has on millions of patients across the globe. Photo courtesty of #MEAction.

More and more individuals are dedicating their time to helping patients have a voice outside of

ME/CFS communities and around the world. And with the help of people today who are advocates, patients are one step closer to educating other people about their disease and witnessing a future that has found the treatments, causes, and cures for ME/CFS.

Resources

The following is a list of organizations that include more information about ME/CFS and are accessible to the public. These organizations are either devoted entirely to research for ME/CFS, support networks for patients from around the world, or provide further details about the disease.

- #ME Action: https://www.meaction.net
- Health Rising: https://www.healthrising.org/
- ME/CFS in Children Fact Sheets: https:// www.cdc.gov/me-cfs/me-cfs-children/ factsheets.htm
- ME Association: http://www.meassociation.org.uk
- ME Research UK: http://www.meresearch.org.uk/
- Nightingale Research Foundation: https://www.nightingale.ca/
- Occupy ME: http://occupyme.net/
- Open Medicine Foundation: https://www.omf.ngo
- Phoenix Rising: https://phoenixrising.me/
- Solve ME/CFS Initiative: https://solvecfs.org

Notes

1. Peter C. Rowe, et al., "Myalgic Encephalo-myelitis/Chronic Fatigue Syndrome Diagnosis and Management in Young People: A Primer," *Frontiers in Pediatrics* 5 (2017): 4, accessed January 15, 2018, doi:10.3389/fped.2017.00121.

2. Ibid.

3. B.M. Carruthers, et al., "Myalgic Encephalo-myelitis: International Consensus Criteria," *Journal of Internal Medicine* 270.4 (2011): 328, accessed January 22, 2018, doi: 10.1111/j.1365-2796.2011.02428.x.

4. "What is ME?" *ME Association* online. Last modified 2018. http://www.meassociation.org.uk/ about/#Part%201.

5. Ibid.

6. Rowe, 8.

7. Ellen W. Clayton, "Beyond Myalgic Encephalo-myelitis/Chronic Fatigue Syndrome: An IOM Report on Redefining an Illness," *JAMA* 313 (2015): 1, accessed February 1, 2018, doi: 10.1001/ jama.2015.1346.

8. Ibid., 2.

9. Ibid., 1.

10. Ibid.

11. Ibid.

12. David S. Bell, *The Disease of a Thousand Names* (Lyndonville, N.Y.: Pollard Publications, 1991).

13. "What is ME?" *ME Association* online. Last modified 2018. http://www.meassociation.org.uk /about/#Part%201.

14. A. G. Gilliam, "Epidemiological Study of an Epidemic, Diagnosed as Poliomyelitis, Occurring Among the Personnel of the Los Angeles County General Hospital During the Summer of 1934," in Public Health Bulletin no.231-240, U.S.

Treasury Department, Public Health Service (1936-1938).

15. Ibid.

16. Byron M. Hyde, *The Clinical and Scientific Basis of Myalgic Encephalomyelitis/Chronic Fatigue Syndrome* (Ogdensburg, N.Y.: Nightingale Research Foundation, 1992).

17. Björn Sigurdsson, et al., "A disease epidemic in Iceland simulating poliomyelitis," *American Journal of Epidemiology* 52, no.2 (1950): 222-238, accessed February 10, 2018, https://doi.org/10.1093/oxfordjournals.aje. a119421.

18. The Medical Staff of the Royal Free Hospital, "An Outbreak of Encephalomyelitis in the Royal Free Hospital Group, London, in 1955," *British Medical Journal* 2.5050 (1957): 895-897.

19. Jill McLaughlin, *Myalgic Encephalomyelitis/Chronic Fatigue Syndrome: An Informational Guidebook for Doctors & Patients* (Ohiopyle, P.A.: Replay Publishing), 1.

20. "Chronic Fatigue Possibly Related to Epstein-Barr Virus—Nevada," *MMWR* online, last modified May 20, 2001, https://www.cdc.gov/mmwr/preview/mmwr   html /00000740.htm.

21. B. D. Scott, "Epidemic Malaise," *British Medical Journal* 1.5689 (1970): 170, accessed February 1, 2018, http://www.ncbi.nlm.nih.gov/pmc/articles/PMC1699088/?page=1.

22. Colin P. McEvedy and A.W. Beard, "Royal Free Epidemic of 1955: A Reconsideration," *British Medical Journal* 1.5687 (1970): 7-11, accessed February 1, 2018, https://www.ncbi.nlm.nih.gov/pmc/articles/PMC1700894/.

23. Rowe, 6.

24. "What is ME/CFS?" *Open Medicine Foundation* online, https://www.omf.ngo/what-is-mecfs/.

25. R.A. Underhill, "Myalgic encephalomyelitis, chronic fatigue syndrome: An infectious disease," *Medical Hypotheses* 85, no.6 (2015): 766-767, accessed January 10, 2018, doi:

10.1016/j.mehy.2015.10.011.

26. Rowe, 8.

27. Ibid., 6.

28. Ibid., 7.

29. Benjamin H. Natelson, "Evidence for the Presence of Immune Dysfunction in Chronic Fatigue Syndrome," *Clinical and Vaccine Immunology* 9, no.4 (2002): 747-752, accessed January 14, 2018, doi: 10.1128/CDLI.9.4.747-752.2002.

30. S.L. Hardcastle, et al., "Longitudinal analysis of immune abnormalities in varying severities of Chronic Fatigue Syndrome/Myalgic Encephalomyelitis patients," *Journal of Translational Medicine* 13 (2015): 299, accessed January 14, 2018, doi: 10.1186/s12967-015-0653-3.

31. Emmanuel A. Ojo-Amaize, "Decreased natural killer cell activity is associated with severity of chronic fatigue immune dysfunction syndrome," *Clinical Infectious Diseases* 18, no.1 (1994): S157-S159, accessed January 14, 2018, https://doi.org/10.1093/clinids/18.Supplement_ 1.S157.

32. Rowe, 6.

33. Ibid.

34. D. Sulheim, et al., "Disease mechanisms and clonidine treatment in adolescent chronic fatigue syndrome: a combined cross-sectional and randomized clinical trial," *JAMA Pediatrics* 168, no.4 (2014): 351-60, accessed January 16, 2018, doi: 10.1001/jamapediatrics. 2013.4647.

35. Rowe, 6.

36. Ibid., 7.

37. D.E. Jones, et al., "Loss of capacity to recover from acidosis on repeat exercise in chronic fatigue syndrome: a case-control study," *European Journal of Clinical Investigation* 42, no.2 (2012): 186-88, accessed January 16, 2018, doi: 10.1111/j.1365-2362.2011.02567.

38. Norman E. Booth, "Mitochondrial dysfunction and the pathophysiology of Myalgic Encephalo-myelitis/Chronic

Fatigue Syndrome (ME/CFS)," *International Journal of Clinical and Experimental Medicine* 5, no.3 (2012): 208-12, accessed January 17, 2018, https://www.ncbi.nlm.nih.gov/pmc/articles/PMC3403556/.

39. Rowe, 7.

40. Ibid.

41. Rosemary A. Underhill and Ruth O'Gorman, "Prevalence of Chronic Fatigue Syndrome and Chronic Fatigue Within Families of CFS Patients," *Journal of Chronic Fatigue Syndrome* 13, no.1 (2006), accessed January 17, 2018, https://doi.org/10.1300/J092v13n01_02.

42. Frederick Albright, et al., "Evidence for a heritable predisposition to Chronic Fatigue Syndrome," *BMC Neurology* 11, no.62 (2011), accessed January 17, 2018, doi: 10.1186/1471-2377-11-62.

43. Rowe, 8.

44. AL Komaroff, et al., "Neurologic Abnormalities in Myalgic Encephalomyelitis/Chronic Fatigue Syndrome: A Review," *Brain and Review* 70, no.1 (2018): 41-54, accessed April 21, 2018, doi: 10.11477/ mf.1416200948.

45. Hidetaka Tanaka, et al., "Impaired postural cerebral hemodynamics in young patients with chronic fatigue with and without orthostatic intolerance," *The Journal of Pediatrics* 140, no.4 (2002): 412-17, accessed February 4, 2018, https://doi.org/10.1067/mpd.2002 .122725.

46. Barry E. Hurwitz, et al., "Chronic fatigue syndrome: illness severity, sedentary lifestyle, blood volume and evidence of diminished cardiac function," *Clinical Science* 118, no.2 (2009): 125-127, accessed January 26, 2018, doi: 10.1042/CS20090055.

47. Jose G. Montoya, et al., "Cytokine signature associated with disease severity in chronic fatigue syndrome patients," *Proceedings of the National Academy of Sciences of the United States of America* (2017) accessed March 17, 2018, doi:

10.1073/pnas.1710519114.

48. Rowe, 5.

49. Ibid.

50. Ibid.

51. Ibid.

52. "Symptoms, testing, and assessment," *ME Association* online. Last modified 2018. http://www.meassociation .org.uk/about/the-symptoms-and-diagnosis-of-mecfs/.

53. Ibid.

54. "Symptoms of ME/CFS," *American Myalgic Encephalomyelitis and Chronic Fatigue Syndrome Society* online. https://ammes.org/symptoms-of-mecfs/.

55. Clayton, ""Beyond Myalgic Encephalomyelitis /Chronic Fatigue Syndrome: An IOM Report on Redefining an Illness," 3.

56. Ibid.

57. Carruthers et al., "Myalgic Encephalomyelitis: International Consensus Criteria," 330.

58. Rowe, 8.

59. Ibid.

60. Mary Dimmock, Susan Levine, and Terri L. Wilder, "Myalgic Encephalomyelitis/Chronic Fatigue Syndrome: What Every Family Physician Needs to Know," *Family Doctor* 6, no. 3 (2018): 23-5, accessed March 15, 2018, http://www.nysafp.org/NYSAFP/media/PDFs/Family%20Do ctor/Family-Physician-Winter-2018WEB.pdf#page=23.

61. Carruthers et al., "Myalgic Encephalomyelitis: International Consensus Criteria," 328-30.

62. Dimmock, "Myalgic Encephalomyelitis/Chronic Fatigue Syndrome: What Every Family Physician Needs to Know," 24.

63. Leonard A. Jason, et al., "A Community-Based Study of Chronic Fatigue Syndrome," *JAMA Internal Medicine* 159, no.18 (1999): 2129-31, accessed January 4, 2018,

doi:10.1001/archinte.159.18.2129.

64. Karen M. Jordan, et al., "Prevalence of pediatric chronic fatigue syndrome in a community-based sample," *Journal of Chronic Fatigue Syndrome* 13, no.2 (2006): 75-8, accessed January 17, 2018, doi: 10.1300/J092v13n02_04.

65. Susanna M. Davies and Esther M. Crawley, "Chronic fatigue syndrome in children aged 11 years old and younger," *Archives of Disease in Childhood* (2008), accessed January 17, 2018, doi: 10.1136/ adc.2007.126649.

66. David S. Bell, Karen Jordan, and Mary Robinson, "Thirteen-Year Follow-Up of Children and Adolescents With Chronic Fatigue Syndrome," *Pediatrics* 107, no.5 (2001): 994-8, accessed January 19, 2018, doi: 10.1542/peds.107.5.994.

67. David S. Bell, "ME/CFS in Children," *Open Medicine Foundation* online, last modified June 25, 2016, https://www.omf.ngo/2016/06/25/mecfs-in-children-by-dr-david-s-bell-2/.

68. Ibid.

69. Rowe, 5-6.

70. Ibid.

71. Elizabeth G. Dowsett and Jane Colby, "Long Term Sickness Absence due to ME/CFS in UK Schools: An Epidemiological Study With Medical and Educational Implications," *Journal of Chronic Fatigue Syndrome* 3, no.2 (1997): 29-32, accessed January 22, 2018, doi: 10.1300/J092v03n02_04.

72. Esther M. Crawley, Alan M. Emond, and Jonathan A. C. Sterne, "Unidentified Chronic Fatigue Syndrome/Myalgic Encephalomyelitis (CFS/ME) is a major cause of school absence: surveillance outcomes from school-based clinics," *BMJ* (2011), accessed January 22, 2018, doi: 10.1136/bmjopen-2011-000252.

73. Rowe, 6.

74. Clayton, "Beyond Myalgic Encephalomyelitis/ Chronic

Fatigue Syndrome: An IOM Report on Redefining an Illness," 3.

75. Ibid.

76. "Myalgic Encephalomyelitis/Chronic Fatigue Syndrome (ME/CFS) Research," in the National Institutes of Health State of Knowledge Workshop Report (2011): 4-5, http://www.meassociation.org.uk/wp-content/uploads/ 2011/08/SoK-Workshop-Report-508-compliant-8-5-11.pdf.

77. Ibid., 10-1.

78. Ibid.

79. Ibid., 16.

80. Julie Rehmeyer, *Through the Shadowlands—A Science Writer's Odyssey into an Illness Science Doesn't Understand* (New York: Rodale Wellness, 2017), 72-3.

81. Bruce Campbell, "Pacing vs. Push and Crash," *CFIDS & Fibromyalgia Self-Help* online, http:// www.cfidsselfhelp.org/library/pacing-vs-push-crash.

82. Leonard A. Jason, et al., "The Energy Envelope Theory and Myalgic Encephalomyelitis/Chronic Fatigue Syndrome," *Workplace Health & Safety* 56, no.5 (2008): 189-95, accessed January 24, 2018, doi:10.1080/ 21641846.2012.733602.

83. Cort Johnson, "Breathe Deep: Dan Moricoli on Yoga and Recovering From Chronic Fatigue Syndrome," *Health Rising* online, last modified April 15, 2015, https://www.healthrising.org/blog/2015/04/15/ breathe-deep-moricoli-yoga-chronic-fatigue-syndrome.

84. Clayton, "Beyond Myalgic Encephalomyelitis/ Chronic Fatigue Syndrome: An IOM Report on Redefining an Illness," 31.

85. Jennifer Spotila, "NIH 2017 Funding Fact-Check," *Occupy ME* online, last modified July 25, 2018, http://occupyme.net/2018/07/23/nih-2017-funding-fact-check/.

86. "Estimates of Funding for Various Research, Condition,

and Disease Categories (RCDC)," *NIH* online, last modified May 18, 2018, https://report .nih.gov/ categorical_spending.aspx.

87. Mary Dimmock, Arthur Mirin, and Jason A. Leonard, "Estimating the disease burden of ME/CFS in the United States and its relation to research funding," *J Med Therap* 1, no.1 (2016): 2-5, accessed March 15, 2018, doi: 10.15761/JMT.1000102.

88. Rowe, 6.

89. Derek Pheby and Lisa Saffron, "Risk factors for severe ME/CFS," *Biology and Medicine* 1, no.4 (2009): 50, accessed January 25, 2018, http://biolmedonline .com Articles/vol1_4_50-74.pdf.

90. Rowe, 6.

91. "What is ME/CFS?" *Open Medicine Foundation* online, https://www.omf.ngo/what-is-mecfs/.

92. Bell, "ME/CFS in Children."

93. Crawley, et al., "Unidentified Chronic Fatigue Syndrome/Myalgic Encephalomyelitis (CFS/ME) is a major cause of school absence: surveillance outcomes from school-based clinics." *BMJ Open* 1, no.2 (2011): e000252, accessed January 25, 2018, doi: 10.1136/ bmjopen-2011-000252.

94. Bell, "ME/CFS in Children."

95. Ibid.

96. Rowe, 12-3.

97. Ibid.

98. Bell, "ME/CFS in Children."

99. Faith Newton, "Myalgic Encephalomyelitis/Chronic Fatigue Syndrome (ME/CFS) School Fact Sheet," in Open Medicine Foundation (2017), accessed January 26, 2018, https://www.omf.ngo/wp-content /uploads/2017/09/ME_CFS-School-Fact-Sheet-Final.pdf.

100. Ibid.

101. Ibid.

Selected Bibliography

Carruthers, B. M. et al. "Myalgic Encephalomyelitis: International Consensus Criteria." *Journal of Internal Medicine* 270.4 (2011): 327–338. *PMC*. Web. 22 January 2018.

Clayton E.W. "Beyond Myalgic Encephalomyelitis/Chronic Fatigue Syndrome: An IOM Report on Redefining an Illness." *JAMA*. 313.11 (2015) :1101–1102. *PMC*. Web. 22 January 2018.

Crawley, Esther M. et al. "Unidentified Chronic Fatigue Syndrome/Myalgic Encephalomyelitis (CFS/ME) is a major cause of school absence: surveillance outcomes from school-based clinics." *BMJ Open*. 1.2 (2011): e000252. *PMC*. Web. 23 January 2018.

Dimmock, M. and Lazell-Fairman, M. "Chronic fatigue syndrome: How to make a disease 'evaporate.'" http://studylib.net/doc/11997986/. (accessed March 15, 2018).

Dimmock, M., Mirin, A., and Jason L. "Estimating the disease burden of ME/CFS in the United States and its relation to research funding." *J Med Therap*. 1.1 (2016): 1-7. *PMC*. Web. 23 January 2018.

Dowsett, Elizabeth G. and Colby J. "Long-Term Sickness Absence Due to ME/CFS in UK Schools." *Journal of Chronic Fatigue Syndrome*. 3.2 (1997): 29-42. *PMC*. Web. 23 January 2018.

Jason, Leonard A. "The Energy Envelope Theory and Myalgic Encephalomyelitis/Chronic Fatigue Syndrome." *Workplace Health & Safety*. 56.5 (2008): 189-195. *PMC*. Web. 24 January 2018.

McLaughlin, J. *Myalgic Encephalomyelitis/Chronic Fatigue Syndrome: An Informational Guidebook for Doctors & Patients*. Pennsylvania: Replay Publishing, 2004.

Rehmeyer, J. *Through the Shadowlands—A Science Writer's Odyssey into an Illness Science Doesn't Understand*. New York: Rodale Wellness, 2017.

Rowe, Peter C. et al. "Myalgic Encephalomyelitis/Chronic Fatigue Syndrome Diagnosis and Management in Young People: A Primer." *Frontiers in Pediatrics* 5 (2017): 121. *PMC*. Web. 22 January 2018.

Acknowledgments

An Adolescent's Guide to ME/CFS was written over the span of two years and couldn't have been possible without the help of many individuals who have tirelessly contributed to the entire process, word by word, draft by draft. To everyone who inspired and encouraged me throughout this journey, my gratitude to you is infinite.

The decision to embark upon this project had actually come out of an assignment I did for my journalism class at school. I had met doctors Dotty and Mark Camenzind, advocates for ME/CFS and parents of Tom Camenzind, a brilliant Stanford student that is currently suffering from severe symptoms of ME/CFS. They educated me about this disease and the significant affect it has on the lives of millions of individuals. When I decided to write an article about this, Dotty and Mark were very supportive of my efforts, providing me with accurate information and clarifying any of my questions on the subject. They continued to encourage me when I began to write *An Adolescent's Guide to ME/CFS* and without their feedback and advice, I would not have been able to finish this book.

Linda Tannenbaum of the Open Medicine Foundation was kind enough to lend her support and made time to look over my drafts in its earliest stages. It was with her insight and connections that writing the most accurate version of my book was possible.

Ben Hsuborger and Adriane Tillman of #MEAction were always very responsive and shared with me the many resources that heavily contributed to the making of this book. I am very grateful for their encouragement and dedication to my efforts.

Julie Rehmeyer was both my inspiration and cheerleader throughout this process. It was after reading her memoir, *Through the Shadowlands*, that I started to see the potential of my idea, and it was through her support that I had began to build upon it. She went through several drafts of my book, always offering suggestions and answering any of my questions.

Mary Dimmock, Leonard Jason, Art Mirin, and Denise Lopez-Majano shared their expertise in the subject and were very thorough in their reviews of my drafts. It was with their knowledge that I was able to check my statements for factual accuracy. I am very grateful for their responsiveness and interest in the book.

I cannot thank organizations like #MEAction, Solve ME/CFS Initiative, and ME Association enough for providing the majority of images in this book. Without their help, I would have been unable to portray the real conditions of many ME/CFS patients. And to the all the patients that took the time and energy to talk to me about their lives, I am so moved by your efforts. Without your dedication, this book wouldn't have been possible.

Tish Davidson was my superhero throughout the entire process of writing this book. She tirelessly read each draft of my book, providing me with advice on how to create the best version of *An Adolescent's Guide to ME/CFS* as possible. Without her, I simply could not have done what I did. I am very thankful that I found such a wonderful developmental editor who had a genuine interest in the work I was doing and who supported me throughout this journey.

Violet Moore was my fantastic copyeditor who helped tremendously in making this book what it is. Without her patience, encouragement, and knowledge, I would not have been able to produce the final (and best) version of this book.

Paula Chinick was my splendid publisher who graciously took a chance on my book. She guided me throughout the entire publishing process, planning every step and detail. She believed in this book as much as I did and for that, I cannot thank her enough.

My parents and sister have been my pillars of support through every single step of the book—from when it was merely an idea to the last word of my manuscript. They kept me motivated and helped me see what was truly important during my hardest times.

About the Author

Vidhima Shetty is a young writer from California who actively seeks to promote the awareness of ME/CFS in her community and around the world.

In 2016, she wrote an article about ME/CFS for her school paper that attained international recognition. After speaking to her school board about the disease and doing more research, she found that most high schools across the nation rarely knew what ME/CFS was and that many adolescents her age with the disease were struggling with their illnesses. She hopes that her efforts will contribute to the propagation of awareness for ME/CFS and patients around the world.

As the founder of The Write Reasons, a writing blog, (thewritereason.org) she is committed to helping other individuals find their passion for writing. Find more about her at vidhimashetty.com.